My Little Book of Thanks

ILLUSTRATED BY

Suzy Spafford

Suzy's Zoo

HARVEST HOUSE PUBLISHERS

EUGENE, OREGON

My Little Book of Thanks

Text Copyright © 2005 by Harvest House Publishers
Eugene, Oregon 97402

ISBN 0-7369-1497-8

Original artwork © Suzy Spafford. Suzy's Zoo® is a registered trade-mark of Suzy's Zoo, A California Corporation.

Design and production by Garborg Design Works, Minneapolis, Minnesota

Harvest House Publishers has made every effort to trace the owner-ship of all poems and quotes. In the event of a question arising from the use of a poem or quote, we regret any error made and will be pleased to make the necessary correction in future editions of this book.

Printed in China

05 06 07 08 09 10 11 / LP / 10 9 8 7 6 5 4 3 2 1

To:

_____

With Love:

_____

I'm so thankful for you!

I am thankful for my home and everything in it, especially my room.

I'm glad our house is a little house,
Not too tall nor too wide;
I'm glad the hovering butterflies
Feel free to come inside.

Our little house is a friendly house,
It is not shy or vain;
It gossips with the talking trees,
And makes friends with the rain.

Christopher Morley

Be grateful for the home you have, knowing that
at this moment, all you have is all you need.

Sarah Ban Breathnach

I am thankful for my mom

Dear God, bless my Mother who
Gives all her life and love to me.
Her heart is tender, calm, and true,
Her faith is boundless as the sea.

John Martin

and dad who love me so much.

God, bless dear Father and please give
Me gratitude to see
How much of all his time and thought
Is given just to me.

John Martin

I am thankful for all the flowers

Be grateful for
the joy of life.

Grenville Kleiser

When flowers bloom, or glad birds sing,
Or trees bend in the breeze,
Go with me, God, and tell me then
That You are loving these.

John Martin

and trees and birds and bees.

I am thankful for the stars at night

For what I have
received, may the
Lord make me truly
thankful. And more
truly for what I have
not received.

Storm Jameson

10

and for the sun that shines so bright.

Dear God, the sky is blue and fair;
The clouds are fleecy white.
The stars shine through the purest air;
The moon is silver bright.

The water runs as clear as glass;
The fragrant breezes greet
The dewy flowers and the grass.
God's world is pure and sweet.

John Martin

I am thankful for my teacher who makes learning a lot of fun.

Let us be grateful to people who make us happy: They are the charming gardeners who make our souls blossom.

Marcel Proust

Dear God, a school-day comes again,
With many things for me to do.
Oh, bless my spirit, heart, and brain,
Making me thoughtful, kind, and true.

John Martin

Sea Shell, Sea Shell,
Sing me a song, O please!
A song of ships, and sailor men,
And parrots, and tropical trees.

Of islands lost in the Spanish Main,
Which no man ever may find again,
Of fishes and corals under the waves,
And sea-horses stabled in great green caves.

Sea Shell, Sea Shell,
Sing of the things you know so well.

Amy Lowell

I am thankful for the sand and sea

Oh, teach me how this bond shall make
Joy, strength, and goodness without end.
And please, dear God, for friendship's sake
Teach me the value of a friend.

John Martin

and for my friends who play with me.

I am thankful for my chores—

We thank God for what He has done for us...We do not complain of what God does not give us; we rather thank God for what He does give us daily...

Dietrich Bonhoeffer

For each new morning with its light,
For rest and shelter of the night,
For health and food, for love and friends,
For everything Thy goodness sends.

Ralph Waldo Emerson

even when they're out of doors.

I am thankful for my fort and

Up in the tree-top, down in the ground,
High in the blue sky, far, all around—
Nearby and everywhere creatures are living,
God in his bounty something giving.

Mary Mapes Dodge

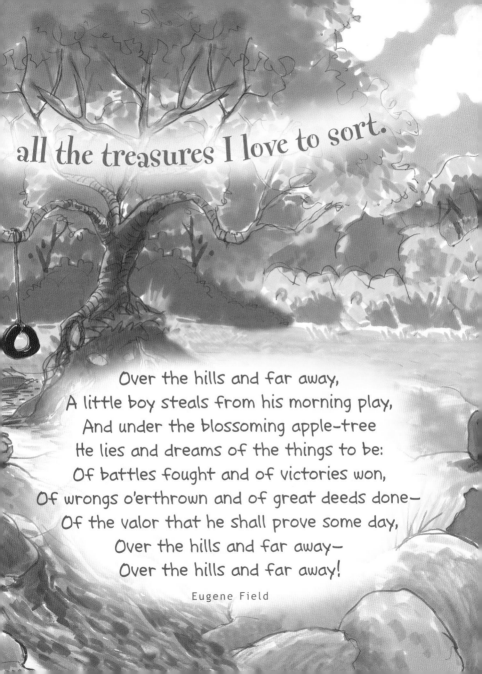

all the treasures I love to sort.

Over the hills and far away,
A little boy steals from his morning play,
And under the blossoming apple-tree
He lies and dreams of the things to be:
Of battles fought and of victories won,
Of wrongs o'erthrown and of great deeds done—
Of the valor that he shall prove some day,
Over the hills and far away—
Over the hills and far away!

Eugene Field

I am thankful for my country and for the land that is home to the free and the brave.

My country 'tis of thee, sweet land of liberty, of thee I sing.

Samuel Smith

I pledge allegiance to the flag
Of United States of America
And to the Republic for which it stands
One nation, under God, indivisible,
With liberty and justice for all.

I am thankful for my health

I thank God for my handicaps, for, through them,
I have found myself, my work, and my God.

Helen Keller

And unto God, for health and food
And all that in thy life is good,
Give thou thy heart in gratitude.

Eugene Field

and for feeling good today.

Thank You, Lord, for my cuddly promise to take good

Mary had a little lamb,
Its fleece was white as snow;
And everywhere that Mary went,
The lamb was sure to go.

He followed her to school one day—
That was against the rule;
It made the children laugh and play,
To see a lamb at school.

Traditional Children's Nursery Rhyme

Every time we remember to say "thank you," we experience nothing less than heaven on earth.

Sarah Ban Breathnach

pets. I love them very much and care of them.

©Suzy Spafford

for all the yummy food we have to eat, especially chocolate chip cookies.

God is great, God is good.
Let us thank Him for our food.
By His hand we all are fed,
Thank You for this daily bread.

Traditional Mealtime Blessing

Butter and toast, cream of corn,
Thank You, Lord, for my cereal this morn.

Veronica Curtis

Thank You, Lord, for blessing me with so many fun and interesting toys. I love all of them!

A house of cards
Is neat and small:
Shake the table,
It must fall.
Find the Court cards
One by one;
Raise it, roof it,—
Now it's done:—
Shake the table!
That's the fun.

Christina Rossetti

When I'm sleepy, I am so

30

©Suzy Spafford

thankful for my soft and comfy bed to lay my head on.

Early to bed,
And early to rise,
Makes a man healthy,
Wealthy and wise.

Old Proverb

Matthew, Mark, Luke, and John
Bless the bed that I lay on!
Four corners to my bed,
Four angels 'round my head,
One at head and one at feet
And two to keep my soul asleep.

Fifteenth-Century Prayer